SCOOBY-DOO!

™

WB

Pedigree®

Published by Pedigree Books Limited. The Old Rectory, Matford Lane, Exeter, EX2 4PS.
Email books@pedigreegroup.co.uk. Published 2002

£5.99

C000183007

GHOULS ON FILM

FRANK STROM--WRITER
JOE STATON--PENCILLER
DAVE HUNT--INKER
JENNA GARCIA--LETTERER
PAUL BECTON--COLORIST
DIGITAL CHAMELEON--SEPARATIONS
HARVEY RICHARDS--ASST. EDITOR
JOAN HILTY--EDITOR

MEANWHILE...

IF THIS *GYONSI* SCAM SHUTS DOWN A *NONGOVERNMENT COMPANY* LIKE GOLDEN HARROW, IT'S A *GOOD* THING!

WOULD THE *GOVERNMENT* DO ANYTHING TO SUPPRESS *INDEPENDENT* COMPANIES?

ARE YOU SUGGESTING THAT *I'M* BEHIND THIS CRIME? A LAWFUL *GOVERNMENT OFFICIAL?!*

BUT I WAS ONLY...!

BAH! I HAVE DUTIES TO ATTEND TO-- GOODBYE!

AND WHAT DUTIES ARE *THOSE,* I WONDER?

TAXI!!

HE'S COME BACK TO *GOLDEN HARROW,* I SEE.

OFFICIAL BUSINESS... OR *MONKEY* BUSINESS?

HMM. DOOR TO THE *WARDROBE TRAILER* IS OPEN. THE PLOT *THICKENS...*

GASP!

HOLY SMOKES! THE *GYONS!!!*

UURRRH...!

NO, NO, NO! YOU DO THE SPINNING ATTACK, AND *YOU* DO THE MIDAIR BACK-FLIP OVER *HIS* HEAD, LANDING *BEHIND* HIM ON *ONE FOOT.* SIMPLE!

LIKE, I'M GETTING POOPED JUST *LISTENING* TO HIM! LET'S TAKE A *BREAK,* SCOOB!

R'OKAY!

ME TOO! I WONDER WHEN WE GET *FED....?*

RI'M *RUNGRY!*

ZOINKS! WE'VE GOT *COMPANY,* SCOOBY, AND IT'S *NOT* THE *CATERER!*

THAT'S *MINA LEUNG*-- BUT WHAT'S *SHE* DOING SNOOPING AROUND HERE?

R'OOK!

SHE'S SNEAKING INTO THE *WARDROBE TRAILER!*

LIKE, THAT MEANS WE'VE GOT OUR *CULPRIT!* I BET SHE'S CHANGING INTO HER *MONSTER COSTUME!*

RAGGY?

HOW 'BOUT THAT! *WE* NABBED THE *BAD GUY* AND DIDN'T GET INTO ANY *TROUBLE* FOR ONCE!

RAGGY?

11

DCSD176

16

DAPHNE'S ROOM...

NO! NOT MY *JOURNAL!*

VELMA'S ROOM...

JINKIES! MY LUCKY *MAGNIFYING GLASS!*

GASP!

YOU WERE *ALL ROBBED?* THAT'S IT! I'M CLOSING DOWN THE HOTEL!

WELL, WE'RE NOT GOING ANYWHERE WITHOUT THE *KEYS* TO THE VAN!

LIKE, CAN WE GET SCOOB ANOTHER COLLAR? HE FEELS *NAKED!*

FROM **MR. CONNERS**, THE HOTEL OWNER ACROSS THE STREET!

IT'S TRUE! YOUR HOTEL HAD BEEN TAKING BUSINESS AWAY FROM MINE FOR TOO LONG! I WANTED YOU OUT OF THE PICTURE!

I'D DO RESEARCH ON ALL THE GUESTS AND FIND OUT WHAT SCARED THEM THE MOST.

JEFFREY GOT ME THE GUEST LIST AND ROOM KEYS. IN EXCHANGE, I'D LET HIM STEAL WHATEVER HE WANTED!

IT WAS A GREAT PLAN! AND WE WOULD HAVE GOT AWAY WITH IT TOO, IF IT WASN'T FOR YOU KIDS AND THAT DOG!

RAN I RAVE RY ROLLAR RACK?

LATER...

I CAN'T THANK YOU ENOUGH. ALL THE STOLEN ITEMS HAVE BEEN RETURNED TO THEIR RIGHTFUL OWNERS--AND THOSE TWO WILL BE GOING AWAY FOR GOOD.

AND THERE SURE WON'T BE ANY MINTS ON THEIR PILLOWS IN **JAIL!**

SPEAKING OF MINTS, ARE WE TOO LATE TO ORDER SOME **ROOM SERVICE?**

HELP YOURSELF TO WHATEVER YOU WANT!

GULP! LIKE, NO OFFENSE, BUT I DON'T WANT TO LOOK AT ANOTHER **BURGER** FOR A LONG, LONG TIME!

I'LL JUST HAVE THE **RIBS, TURKEY, CLUB SANDWICH, FONDUE, SUSHI, KEBABS...**

HA HA HA HA HA

ROOBY ROOBY ROO!

THE END

DRAW A CONCLUSION
WHO ATE ALL THE SANDWICHES?

To identify the thief, draw the contents of each box in the grid below.
Use the coordinates to locate the correct position of each piece.

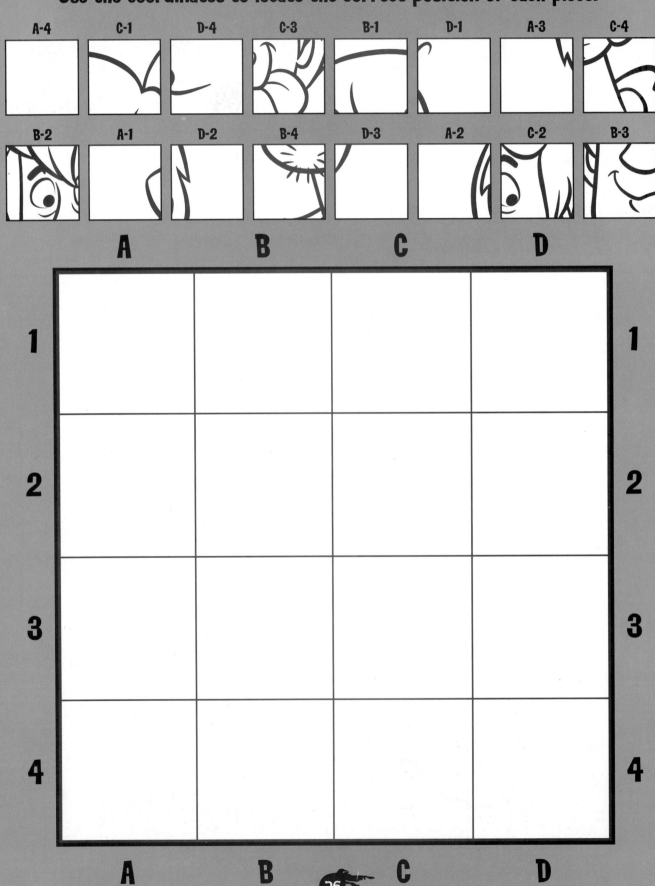

THE CASE OF THE CINEMA SPIRIT

CHUCK DIXON-Writer
JOE STATON-Penciller
MIKE DeCARLO-Inker
SERGIO GARCIA-Letterer
PAUL BECTON-Colorist
DIGITAL CHAMELEON-Separations
HARVEY RICHARDS-Asst Editor
JOAN HILTY-Editor

SCOOBY-DOO 56. March, 2002. Published monthly by DC Comics, 1700 Broadway, New York, NY 10019. POSTMASTER: Send address changes to SCOOBY-DOO, DC Comics Subscriptions, P.O. Box 0528, Baldwin, NY 11510. Annual subscription rate $23.88. Canadian subscribers must add $12.00 for postage and GST. GST # is R125921072. All foreign countries must add $12.00 for postage. U.S. funds only. Copyright © 2002 Hanna-Barbera. All Rights Reserved. SCOOBY-DOO and all related characters and elements depicted herein are trademarks of and copyrighted by Hanna-Barbera. CARTOON NETWORK and logo are trademarks of Cartoon Network. The stories, characters and incidents mentioned in this magazine are entirely fictional. Printed on recyclable paper. Printed in Canada. DC Comics. A division of Warner Bros.—An AOL Time Warner Company

ALL THAT LOOT FOR SOME OLD *BOX?*

NOT JUST *ANY* BOX, SHAG.

HASSENFUS WAS A SCREEN *LEGEND*—AND A *GENIUS* AT MAKE-UP AND OPTICAL EFFECTS!

HE COULD PLAY *ANYTHING*, FROM A MONSTER TO A LEADING MAN.

SO HOW COME I NEVER *HEARD* OF HIM?

MOST OF HIS FILMS ARE FROM THE *SILENT* ERA.

AND THERE ISN'T AN EXISTING PRINT OF *ANY* OF THEM.

THEY'RE ALL *LOST* TO--

JINKIES!

OH!

MARIA...YOU MUST HELP ME FIND MARIA...

RAT'S ROUBLE!

LIKE, *NO* HITCHHIKERS, MAN!

THANKS FOR *SEEING* US, MR. HASSENFUS.

I UNDERSTAND YOU *BOUGHT* SOMETHING OF MINE AT TODAY'S AUCTION.

YES—YOUR OLD MAKE-UP CASE, SIR.

YOU STARRED IN *ALL* OF THESE MOVIES, MR. HASSENFUS?

THESE AND *MANY* MORE.

PIRATE'S BRIDE

THE CAVALIER WAY

ARGENTINE FURY

THE LADY AND THE COSSACK

AND ALL PRINTS ARE GONE?

FOREVER, I'M AFRAID.

BUT THOSE WERE GOLDEN DAYS.

EVERYONE KNEW MY NAME.

THE PIRATE'S BRIDE

HARD TO BELIEVE I WAS *EVER* THAT YOUNG, EH?

HARD TO BELIEVE...

MY OLD MAKE-UP CASE. YOU SAY THERE'S A PROBLEM WITH IT?

NOT A PROBLEM *EXACTLY*.

MORE LIKE IT'S, LIKE, *HAUNTED*.

RUM DE DUM DE DUM...

♪♪♭♪ ♪♪♪♪♭♪ ♪♪♪♪♭♪ ♪♪♪♪

!!

ROOPS!

WELL, SCOOBY, YOUR *WHISTLING* CERTAINLY HAS AN EFFECT ON PEOPLE!

WHAT'S GOING ON HERE?

SCOOBY WAS WHISTLING AND THIS ACTRESS JUST *FAINTED.*

EVERYONE KNOWS IT'S CONSIDERED *VERY UNLUCKY* TO WHISTLE BACKSTAGE!

THEY'RE NERVOUS *ENOUGH* ABOUT THE GHOST...AND YOUR FRIEND AND THE DOG AREN'T HELPING!

I'M SORRY, MR. LOVEY -- HONESTLY, SHAGGY AND SCOOBY *ARE* ONLY TRYING TO *HELP*...

45

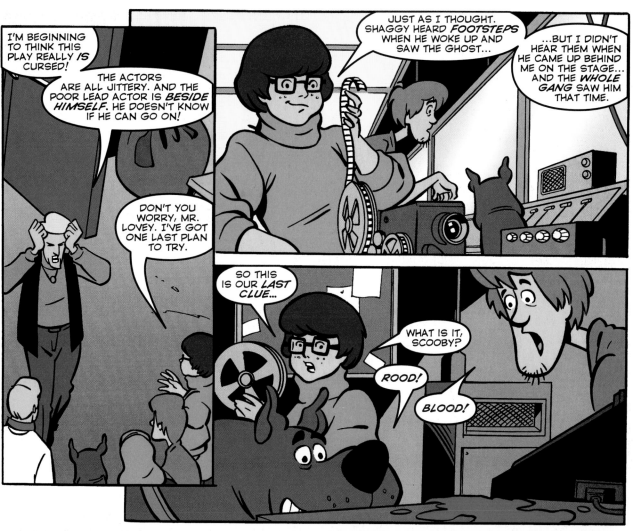

"...IN EVERY WAY THEY *KNOW HOW* TO!"
ZZZ! ZZZZ! ZZZ!
THUNK
THUNK
LIKE, *WHO'S THERE?*
YAAAAAHHH!!
HELP! LIKE, *THERE'S THE GHOST!*
LIKE, I SAW HIM, SCOOB!
HE WAS ON THE STAGE! I WOKE UP AND THERE HE WAS!
RIKES, RAGGY!
LIKE, ALL THIS EXCITEMENT IS MAKING ME *HUNGRY!*
WHAT SAY WE FIND THE CAFETERIA AND GET SOMETHING TO EAT?
REAH RAGGY, RET'S REAT!

I'M BEGINNING TO THINK THIS PLAY REALLY *IS* CURSED!

THE ACTORS ARE ALL JITTERY. AND THE POOR LEAD ACTOR IS *BESIDE HIMSELF.* HE DOESN'T KNOW IF HE CAN GO ON!

DON'T YOU WORRY, MR. LOVEY. I'VE GOT ONE LAST PLAN TO TRY.

JUST AS I THOUGHT. SHAGGY HEARD *FOOTSTEPS* WHEN HE WOKE UP AND SAW THE GHOST...

...BUT I DIDN'T HEAR THEM WHEN HE CAME UP BEHIND ME ON THE STAGE... AND THE *WHOLE GANG* SAW HIM THAT TIME.

SO THIS IS OUR *LAST CLUE...*

WHAT IS IT, SCOOBY?

ROOD!

BLOOD!

LIKE, YEUCH!

IT'S NOT *REAL* BLOOD, GUYS--IT'S THE *STAGE BLOOD* THE ACTORS USE.

LOOK, THERE'S MORE ON THE FLOOR!

IT LOOKS LIKE A *TRAIL...*

BUT WHO COULD IT BE?

LET'S FIND OUT!

IT'S AN *UNDERSTUDY*... BUT WHY?

AFTER FINDING THE NOTE AND THE DAGGER IN THE *STAR'S* DRESSING ROOM, I'D GUESS HE'S JEALOUS.

YOU MEAN HE WANTED TO PLAY MACBETH SO BADLY THAT HE TRIED TO TERRIFY MY STAR ACTOR?

AND HE NEARLY SCARED AWAY *ALL* MY ACTORS!

BUT HOW DID HE MOVE AROUND SO QUICKLY?

THAT'S THE *CLEVER* PART.

HE MADE A *FILM* OF HIMSELF IN COSTUME AND PROJECTED IT ONTO THE STAGE!

THAT'S WHY WE DIDN'T HEAR HIS *FOOTSTEPS* --AND WHY *YOU* DIDN'T NOTICE THE *COSTUME* WAS MISSING...

...UNTIL *SHAGGY* SAW THE REAL THING WHEN HE USED IT BETWEEN REHEARSALS!

I ONLY WANTED TO BE A STAR... JUST *ONCE*.

WELL, YOU'D BE A STAR IN THE *SPECIAL EFFECTS* DEPARTMENT, BUT NOT BEFORE YOU'VE PUT THIS MESS RIGHT!

LO, THE PERFORMANCE BEGINS...

LIKE, IT'S THE DUDE WITH THE DAGGER AGAIN!

REAH, RAGGY. RHIS IS RARY!

LIKE, DON'T WORRY, SCOOB. THEY DON'T NEED YOUR TONGUE, THEY'VE GOT ONE OF THEIR *OWN!*

RUH! RUKKY!

AND I'D LIKE TO THANK MY YOUNG FRIENDS HERE FOR MAKING THIS PRODUCTION OF *MACBETH* POSSIBLE!

LIKE, WHERE'S THE ACTOR IN THE SHAKESPEARE COSTUME?

WHAT? WE DON'T HAVE AN ACTOR PLAYING SHAKESPEARE.

YIKES!

LIKE, MAYBE *SHAKESPEARE* WANTED TO STOP THE JINX TOO?

ENCORE, SCOOBY! ENCORE!

HA! HA! HA!

HA!

THE END

50

WRITER: DAN ABNETT

PENCILS: ANTHONY WILLIAMS

INKS: JEFF ALBRECHT

LETTERER: JENNA GARCIA

COLORIST: PAUL BECTON

SEPARATOR: DIGITAL CHAMELEON

ASST. EDITOR: HARVEY RICHARDS

EDITOR: JOAN HILTY

LADIES, GENTLEMEN... CAN I TAKE YOU TO YOUR HOTEL, PERHAPS?

WHY DON'T YOU AND *DAPHNE* GO AHEAD WITH THE LUGGAGE, FRED? WE'LL FOLLOW ON FOOT.

OH, *LET'S,* FREDDY! IT'LL BE *SO ROMA--*

--I MEAN, FUN.

MY, THIS IS *LOVELY,* ISN'T IT, FREDDY?

SURE IS, DAPH!

SAY, FRIEND! HAVE YOU HEARD ANYTHING ABOUT A *PHANTOM GONDOLIER?*

JUST A MYTH, SIGNORE--AN *OLD* STORY!

THERE CAN BE A *LOT* TO THOSE OLD TALES, SIR.

HMPH! MORE INTERESTED IN THE *GHOST,* AS USUAL!

BWA-HA-HA-HA!

MAMA MIA! NOT *AGAIN!*

WOW!

YIKES!

YOU KNOW ABOUT THAT, SIGNORE?

VENICE IS THE CITY OF LOVE, BUT THE LOVERS, THEY ARE STAYING AWAY!

SOON I WILL GO OUT OF BUSINESS... THEN NO MORE GELATO!

IT IS ALL THE FAULT OF THE *PHANTOM*...

...A GONDOLIER COME BACK TO *HAUNT* THE CITY. HE HAS FRIGHTENED AWAY ALL THE LOVERS. IT IS *TERRIBLE!*

DON'T YOU WORRY, SIGNORE-- *WE'LL* PUT THIS PHANTOM GONDOLIER OUT OF BUSINESS! WON'T WE, GANG?

RIGHT *RON*, *RELMA!*

THANKS, SCOOB.

RACTUALLY, RAT RAS RAGGY...

THE NEXT EVENING...

WE DIDN'T FIND MUCH--EXCEPT THIS *SASH* ON ONE OF THE BRIDGES.

IT IS VERY *OLD!* MAYBE IT BELONGS TO THE PHANTOM!

CAN YOU GUYS TAKE US BACK TO WHERE YOU FOUND IT?

CAFE

HEY SHAGGY! SCOOBY! NO TIME FOR FOOD NOW! THERE'S A *MYSTERY* WAITING!

BUT IT'S LIKE, *DINNERTIME!* IF IT WAS REALLY TIME FOR A MYSTERY, THEY'D CALL IT, LIKE, *"MYSTERY-TIME"!*

WE'LL GET SOMETHING TO EAT *LATER!*

MENU

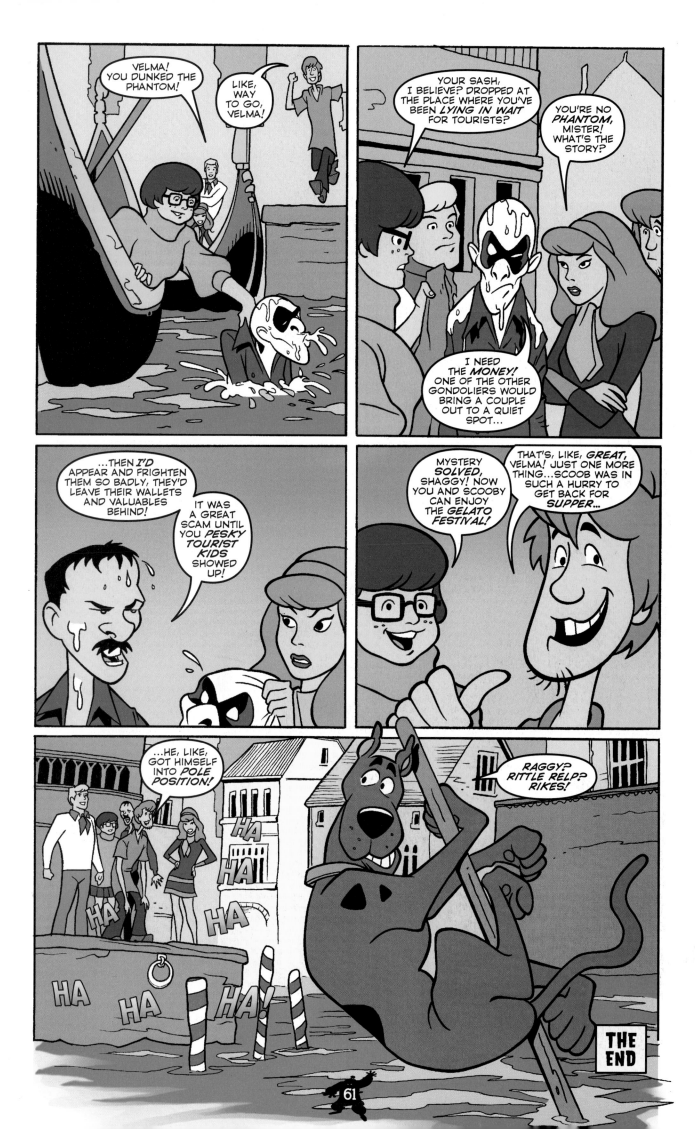